Where Are You Going, Aja Rose?

Story by Joy Cowley

"Where are you going, Aja Rose?"

"I'm going to stand on my head."

"Where are you going, Aja Rose?"

"I'm going to jump on the bed."

"Where are you going, Aja Rose?"

"I'm going to fly a plane."

"Where are you going, Aja Rose?"

"I'm going to drink the rain."

"Where are you going, Aja Rose?"
"I'm going to build a house."

10

"Where are you going, Aja Rose?"
"I'm going to feed my mouse."

11

"Where are you going, Aja Rose?"

"I'm going to climb a tree."

"Can we come with you, Aja Rose?"

"I'd love you to come with me!"